GRADE 2

The Syllabus of Examinations s
requirements, especially those
sight-reading. Attention shoul
Notices on the inside front cove
any changes.

The syllabus is obtainable from music retailers or from
The Associated Board of the Royal Schools of Music,
24 Portland Place, London W1B 1LU, United Kingdom
(please send a stamped addressed C5 (162mm x 229mm)
envelope).

In examination centres outside the UK, information and
syllabuses may be obtained from the Local Representative.

CONTENTS

Where appropriate, pieces in this volume have been checked with original source material
and edited as necessary for instructional purposes. Fingering, phrasing, pedalling,
metronome marks and the editorial realization of ornaments (where given) are for
guidance only; they are not comprehensive or obligatory.

Editor for the Associated Board: **Richard Jones**

DO NOT
PHOTOCOPY
© MUSIC

Alternative pieces for this grade

Music origination by Barnes Music Engraving Ltd.
Cover by Økvik Design.
Printed in England by Headley Brothers Ltd,
The Invicta Press, Ashford, Kent.

Air in C

BLOW

John Blow (1649–1708) was organist of Westminster Abbey from 1668, a post he relinquished in 1679 to make way for his pupil Henry Purcell (he was reinstated after Purcell's death in 1695), and a Gentleman of the Chapel Royal from 1674. In this air, all slurs and dynamics are editorial suggestions only. The original ornament signs have been replaced by their modern equivalents. The source has a turn to the RH second crotchet of bb. 1, 3, 5 and 9. The ornament in b. 7 is optional for the purposes of the examination. Unslurred quavers might be lightly detached.
Source: London, British Library, Add. MS 22099

© 1991 by The Associated Board of the Royal Schools of Music
Adapted from *Baroque Keyboard Pieces*, Book I, edited by Richard Jones (Associated Board)

Gavotte in F

A:2

DUSSEK

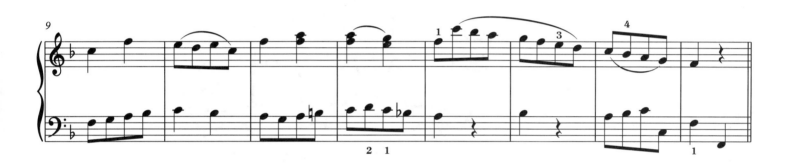

Jan Ladislav Dussek (1760–1812) was born into a Bohemian family of musicians. He led an international career: after studying in Prague, he found employment in Paris and London, and toured as a virtuoso pianist in Holland, Germany and Russia. In this gavotte, all slurs and dynamics are editorial suggestions only. Unslurred crotchets might be lightly detached.
Source: *Dussek's Instructions on the Art of Playing the Piano Forte or Harpsichord* (London & Edinburgh, 1796)

© 2002 by The Associated Board of the Royal Schools of Music

Menuet in D

No. 10 from *Nannerl-Notenbuch*

L. MOZART

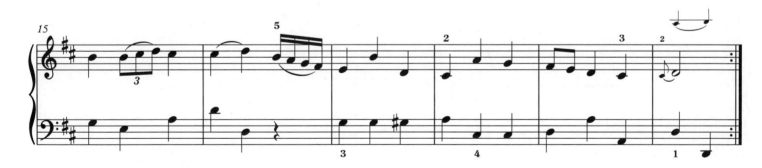

Nannerl-Notenbuch Notebook for Nannerl

This piece is drawn from a collection that Leopold Mozart compiled in 1759 for his eight-year-old daughter Maria Anna, nicknamed Nannerl. Her younger brother Wolfgang Amadeus soon began to play some of the pieces himself: according to his father, he had mastered 10 of them by the age of 4. In this minuet, the slur in b. 2, together with its equivalents elsewhere, is original; other slurs and all dynamics are editorial suggestions only.

Source: L. Mozart: *Nannerl-Notenbuch*, 1759; original manuscript, property of the Internationale Stiftung Mozarteum, Salzburg

Allegretto

First movement from Sonatina in C, Op. 136 No. 1

B:1

REINECKE

Carl Reinecke (1824–1910) was for many years conductor of the celebrated Leipzig Gewandhaus Orchestra and professor of piano and composition at the Leipzig Conservatory, where his pupils included Grieg and Sullivan. His huge output includes many piano pieces in the style of Schumann. This Allegretto is a miniature sonata-form movement: it includes a forthright first subject in the tonic key (bb. 1–8), a more cantabile second subject in the dominant (b. 9), a canonic development in the minor mode (b. 17), a recapitulation of the first subject (b. 25) and finally of the second subject (b. 33), now transposed to the tonic.

Source: *Sechs Miniatur-Sonaten*, Op. 136 (Leipzig: Breitkopf & Härtel, 1875)

B:2

Un gros chagrin

No. 5 from *Pour les petits*

Edited by
Lionel Salter

SANDRÉ

Un gros chagrin A Great Sorrow; **Pour les petits** For the Little Ones

Gustave Sandré (1843–1916) was a French composer and pianist. This piece is drawn from his collection of piano pieces for the young entitled *Pour les petits,* which appeared as a supplement to the magazine *L'illustration* at Christmas 1896.

Reproduced from *Short Romantic Pieces for Piano*, Book I, edited by Lionel Salter (Associated Board)

Gukkuk im Versteck

No. 4 from Appendix of *Album für die Jugend*, Op. 68

Edited by
Howard Ferguson

SCHUMANN

B:3

Gukkuk im Versteck Cuckoo in Hiding; **Album für die Jugend** Album for the Young

Schumann's *Album für die Jugend* was composed in less than a month in 1848. At the time, the composer wrote: 'I don't remember ever having been in such good musical form . . . The pieces simply poured out, one after another.' Some of them were dedicated to his daughter Marie on her seventh birthday. In this piece, although no opening dynamic is given, note Schumann's instruction above the first bar to always play very quietly. The *pp* markings are original.
Source: part-autograph MS, Robert-Schumann-Haus, Zwickau

Reproduced from Schumann: *Album für die Jugend*, Op. 68, edited by Howard Ferguson (Associated Board)

C:1

Somewhere near Cluj

JULIAN ANDERSON

The composer has written: 'This piece uses a simple, folk-type melody, somewhat reminiscent of the traditional music found in the region of Cluj in Romania.' Pedalling is left to the player's discretion.

Reproduced from *Spectrum 2: 30 Miniatures for Solo Piano* (Associated Board) by permission. All enquiries for this piece apart from the examinations should be addressed to Faber Music Ltd, 3 Queen Square, London WC1N 3AU.

March Hare

No. 5 from *In the Pink*

C:2

BRIAN CHAPPLE

The composer has written: ' "March Hare" looks more difficult than it is: do not forget that the quavers, whether staccato or legato, move at exactly the same speed in every bar.'

Herbie Funky

from *Les enfants du jazz*

VINCENT HUET

The dynamics are editorial suggestions only.

Reproduced by permission of Editions Salabert/United Music Publishers Ltd. All enquiries for this piece apart from the examinations should be addressed to United Music Publishers Ltd, 42 Rivington Street, London EC2A 3BN.